THE DOLPHIN'S DREAM
HEALING TALES AND STORIES FOR YOUNG PEOPLE

By Donald Brooks Mason

Illustrated by Donald Brooks Mason
Edited by Sandy Grubb Chapman
Cover Art by Kenya J. Barnett

Prairie Schooner Publishing Company
Shaker Heights, Ohio
1998

Prairie Schooner Publishing Company
3709 Glencairn Road
Shaker Heights, Ohio 44122

TO PARENTS

As a parent you should be advised that some of these stories contain themes and imagery which may be unsettling to some young people. This is not an undesirable reaction, however, because these stories have been written to help young people deal in a positive way with troubling situations in their lives. In all cases, therefore, you should read these stories before sharing them with your children. And in all cases, you should encourage your children to discuss their reactions to the stories.

DBM

to Charlotte
Maureen
Mariah
Aaron
and Ruth

ACKNOWLEDGEMENTS

Accomplishments such as this book come about through the efforts of many people. That is certainly true for this one. Special thanks are in order for Nicholas Diederich, and Kyle and Todd LaBerge who were the first audience to hear these stories.

My experiences with Barry Neil Kaufman and the staff of the Option Institute in Sheffield, Massachusetts helped shape the messages in these stories.

Had I not attended my high school class reunion last year I would not have had the good fortune of having Sandy Grubb Chapman become my editor. Her loving attention to her task has made this a better book.

Charlotte Mason, my life's partner, has read, listened to, and discussed every story with me countless times. Every page and every drawing has been enriched by her love and wisdom. This is her book almost as much as it is mine.

Thank you all.

PREFACE

Marbles, Jackie, Austin, Caliph, the Tiger, and the other principal characters of these stories are modeled on children and young people whom I have come to know through my years as a social worker. Though some of them experienced unwelcome family problems — even abuse and neglect—all of them had in common the challenges and opportunities of living: understanding and coming to terms with fears and judgments about themselves, other persons, and events; experiencing the losses of family, friends, possessions, and dreams unfulfilled; learning to trust; living with peer pressures — and more. For this reason I believe these stories are appropriate for a wide range of young people. The single criterion in deciding if a story is appropriate for a particular child or young person is whether or not she or he expresses interest in the story.

The tales and stories of this book were written to convey messages which can connect with a young listener's inner knowing. They carry two primary messages. The first is that everyone is special. All people are perfect as they are; they need not do anything to increase their value, nor can they become less valuable.

The second message is that everyone is trying to be happy, even though people sometimes adopt beliefs which cause them to be unhappy instead. But beliefs are changeable—and anyone can decide to make a change.

These are stories that must be read aloud. Their sentence structures, vocabulary, and cadences represent the way I talk when telling them. You, the story reader/teller, should feel free to make the small adjustments in these stories which allow you to be comfortable with them and allow them to become your stories. Play with them and give them the accents and emphases which bring them alive and free their messages to be heard by your listeners.

Please be alert to any signs that the listener doesn't understand the story or certain words or expressions—especially with very young children. When necessary, pause to explain the action of a story or to explain a word or phrase. Insert other words or expressions which will increase the listener's comprehension and with which you may be more comfortable.

If you are a parent, you should understand that healing stories such as these are not the same as bedtime stories. Children should be encouraged to talk about their thoughts and feelings about the stories. You should therefore choose places and times for reading these stories which allow for "processing" (as it is called) to take place.

Helping persons, such as social workers, counselors, teachers, ministers, art therapists, and psychologists, should also make the processing of the stories a priority. Again, repeated telling of the selected stories will increase the healing powers of their messages.

The messages of these stories travel on the enjoyment of the stories themselves. Every person is special and we all have the capacity to choose beliefs which will produce our own happiness. It is my hope that your audiences will be entertained and intrigued by these stories.

CONTENTS

Acknowledgements vii

Preface ix

1. **Marbles' Story** 1
Marbles didn't need anyone to tell her that she
was a problem, because she knew it. She could
not or would not stop touching other parrots her
age and would not stop blurting out embarrassing remarks which made the other parrots in her
class laugh.

2. **The Boy and the Junkyard Dog** 5
They stood there in a nervous silence eying
one another, not knowing whether to trust each other.

3. **A Mother to Love Me** 9
Jackie told Nannie how much she wanted a real
mother. One who would sit and talk with her,
brush the tangles from her hair, make good dinners and cookies, laugh and play with her, make
pretty curtains for her bedroom window, and hug
her everyday — like Nannie did with Seneca.

4. **Austin Learns About Seizures** 15
Things were starting to make sense for Austin
now that his mom was telling him about the
seizures she and his dad sometimes had.

5. **The Dolphin's Dream** 21
The dolphin resented that the other young dol-
phins in the family should have been so lucky as
to be with their real parents. He felt angry and
hurt, as if there was something <u>wrong</u> with him.

xi

6. Two Brother Lions **27**

"Shut up!" screamed the younger brother. "I
don't want you as my brother!" he snarled.
"Untie that rope and let me go!"

7. Hilton's Knocking Knees **31**

It was Promotion Day for pelicans in the Glider
Class. Hilton knew he would not be promoted
unless he could dive into the sea and he was
afraid to dive.

8. Hen and Her Duck **35**

Hen loved Duck very much. She wanted Duck
to be just like her and she wanted to be just
like Duck.

9. Help for Caliph **39**

Each time the wolf came he poked and pushed
the pups in ways that didn't feel right to them.
When Caliph finally said, "Stop, don't play that
way," and "I want to go home," the older wolf
laughed and called him a sissy. Then he lowered his head and said . . . "You can't go back
now because I'll tell on you, and your mother
will be angry and punish you."

10. Ben's Story **43**

The water in the bowl sloshed gently back
and forth causing the two goldfish floating
on top to glisten in the morning sun like
two maple leaves fallen from a branch
in the fall. Now, Ben had to decide how
to say good-bye to his fish.

11. **Special Kitten** **47**

The kittens were only a week old when Darnell
noticed that one of the white kittens had a short
front leg. The kitten stumbled and fell down
more than the others... Darnell worried that the
kitten might not live, or might not be able to
take care of itself like the others could.

12. **The Boy and the Crow** **53**

There once lived a boy with his family in a
house next to a woods. One morning when he
and his friends were playing he ran into the
woods and lost his way among the trees. He
could no longer see or hear his friends. The boy
was lost.

13. **The Unhappy Princess** **57**

The princess told her fairy godmother that she
was unhappy because nothing was like she
wanted it to be. When the fairy godmother asked
what it was that wasn't as she wanted it to be the
princess put her head down and cried, "I can't
say."

14. **When the Tiger Believes** **63**

Ever since that terrifying night the voices of the
raging hyenas have echoed in the tiger's head.
They tell him he is under a spell he can never
break; that demons live inside him.

15. **The Mouse Who Was
Afraid of the Dark** **67**

There once was a little mouse who slept

in a baby's shoe. As cozy as the shoe was,
it did not keep the mouse from becoming
afraid of the dark.

16. Brother Alligator Learns a Lesson 71
Late one summer afternoon when the sun
was hanging low over the willow trees,
Brother Rabbit heard Brother Alligator
talking. Brother Alligator was talking
about catching him, that very night.

17. A Tale of Two Partridges 77
Quilla did not want to live with another family.
She had already lived with a turkey, a cat, and a
hen. "I was supposed to have a partridge for a
mother. It's just not fair," she said.

18. Burley's Father 85
Burley remembered that awful fight and how
his father had looked back at Burley's mother
lying there on the ground. He had been very
young at the time. Now Grandma Neerja was
telling him about his father.

19. Jerry Jump 91
Jerry had his 9th birthday, his 10th, 11th, 12th,
14th, 15th birthdays. He was growing up. He
was jumping ever higher. But, Jerry Jump was
not growing tall.

20. Grubb's Story 95
Grubb did not mind being a chubby green and
yellow snake nearly as much as she minded
being teased about being chubby.

APPENDIX 103

MARBLES' STORY

"And now ladies and gentlemen, boys and girls, Tillby's Traveling Circus proudly presents the awesome, the magnificent, the extraordi-naire—Miss Molly's Performing Parrots!" announced the barker.

No sooner had the sixteen green parrots begun their act than pandemonium erupted. The sixteen parrots had been sitting shoulder to shoulder on a long white perch. Parrot number 8, the one called Marbles, began flapping her wings in the faces of the parrots sitting next to her. When she stopped flapping her wings, she reached behind her and bit the tail of parrot number 7 and began calling out in a raucous voice, "Make my day, baby! Come on over. Let's bump beaks."

1

In a second, parrots were flying round the tent causing spectators to duck and run from their seats as the birds swooped down grabbing for hats and popcorn bags.

Miss Molly, the trainer, was frantically calling to the now startled and angry parrots: "Cuba, Phibbe, Crackers . . . come to Momma!" Circus helpers were there with nets in no time trying to catch the careening parrots. The very first parrot they went for was number 8, the one called Marbles.

Once the parrots were back in their cages backstage there was a hubbub of talk, all of it about Marbles being the biggest problem in the circus.

Marbles didn't need anyone to tell her that she was a problem because she knew it. Right from when she was a little parrot she had been taken to one trainer after another. She could not, or would not, stop touching other parrots her age. She would not stop blurting out embarrassing remarks which made the other parrots in her class laugh. Sometimes she would get mad and threaten to hit the ones who laughed, which only made them mad and made things worse. Mr. Tillby, the owner of the circus, would send her to her cage at those times.

To those trainers she trusted, Marbles would always say the same thing: "Tell me what I should do! Please tell me what I should do! I want to stop doing these things." Sometimes they would make a suggestion, but whatever they suggested didn't help. Marbles could never keep from bothering the other parrots for very long.

Marbles thought Miss Molly was more helpful than anyone she knew. Miss Molly would never criticize her. She usually didn't try to tell her what she should do. Instead she would say things like, "You won't always act this way. You just have to grow some. When you're ready to change, you'll be able to." Marbles didn't really know what Miss Molly meant, but after listening to her she always felt like she could try again.

It was a struggle for Marbles to change the way she acted, even with Miss Molly's help. After the big commotion that night at the circus show Marbles was asked to sit on a perch with just two of the other parrots. They were off to the side, away from the main bunch. The three of them had a rope-climbing trick to do and they usually did it fine. But sometimes Marbles would pull on the tail of the parrot ahead of her or start calling out something like, "Look at me! Aren't I gorgeous!" The act didn't go so well when she did things like that.

Though Marbles still had her problems, she kept trying to change. Whenever she felt like she would never be able to act any better, she would remember Miss Molly's words:

"You won't always do these things.
You just have to grow some.
And then, when you're ready to change,
you'll be able to."

THE BOY AND THE JUNKYARD DOG

TUESDAY

There they stood, three boys raking sticks across a chain link fence, shouting, "Come and get us, you stupid mongrels," trying to frighten the three dogs on the other side of the fence. Barking, snarling, and snapping back at the boys were three junkyard guard dogs. On the side of the dogs' house, in full view for the boys to see, was a sign which read, "BEWARE! VICIOUS JUNKYARD DOGS."

One boy said, "I don't think we ought to be doing this. It's mean . . . and besides they're just dogs."

"Vicious Junkyard Dogs is what they are!" replied one of his friends. "Yeah, can't you read?" said the other friend.

One of the barking dogs wagged his tail while he barked. The other two dogs just curled their lips higher to show more of their teeth with each raking of the sticks across the chain links of the fence.

WEDNESDAY

There stood the boy who had said he thought it was mean to tease the dogs, holding a ball of kite twine connected to a kite which lay on the ground. The boy and his kite were separated by the chain link fence of the junkyard. Outside the fence stood the boy. On the other side of the fence, in the junkyard, lay the kite. Standing next to the kite was the dog who had wagged his tail.

Facing the boy was the doghouse with its red-lettered sign, "BEWARE! VICIOUS JUNK-YARD DOGS."

Each time the boy moved, the junkyard dog barked wildly. When the boy stood still, the dog stopped barking. It would stand still too, except for an almost imperceptible wagging of the white tip of its tail. These small wags were noticed by the boy. Between the dog and the boy was a gate.

On the ground next to the gate was a padlock which had once been used to lock the gate. The gate was now unlocked. The boy could have easily retrieved his kite by opening the gate and reaching inside to pick it up, were it not for the fact that the dog stood there next to the kite. What was he to do?

The boy thought to himself, "If only I hadn't hit the fence and yelled like my friends. I didn't really want to scare the dogs. He thinks I want to hurt him. If I open the gate the dog might bite me."

The dog thought to himself, "If only I hadn't snarled and snapped at the boys like my friends. He thinks I'm really vicious and will bite him if he opens the gate If he opens the gate I am afraid he will hit me."

Then the boy thought, "This dog wags his tail when he barks. He wagged it yesterday and he's wagging it now. Maybe he's not like the other dogs. Maybe he won't bite."

At the same moment the dog thought, "This boy told his friends he didn't think they should be hitting the fence and yelling at us. He isn't doing those things now. Maybe he isn't like the other boys."

The boy put his hand on the gate latch. He hesitated. He still hadn't made up his mind to open the gate.

Seeing the boy reach for the latch, the junkyard dog stiffened his body, growled low in his throat, and moved closer to the gate.

They stood there in a nervous silence eying one another, not knowing whether to trust each other.

Then the boy made up his mind. "This dog is different from the others. He doesn't want to bite me." He spoke softly to the junkyard dog, "Hey fella, I won't hurt you. I just want my kite." He put his hand on the gate latch, lifted it, and swung it partway open.The dog had to make his decision—attack or let the boy through the gate. He gave a single sharp bark. Then, beginning with small tip-of-the-tail wags which quickly grew into the wide wags of a friend, he greeted the boy.

The boy got his kite that day. The junkyard dog got a good rub between the ears. Both of them made a friend. They both got what they had really wanted all along because they did what they thought was best for them and acted like themselves.

A MOTHER TO LOVE ME

"Listen child! You'd better do as I say. I told you to pick up your clothes from off the floor!" Grandma Roberts was upset. Her mouth was drawn tight with that exasperated look she got when Jackie hadn't done something she had told her to do.

"I don't know what's to become of you, Jackie. You don't do anything anybody tells you—not me, not your teachers in school." Grandma paused and then with a long sigh turned and walked away saying, "Cain't nobody help this child the way she is."

Jackie had that feeling low in her stomach that she got whenever Grandma Roberts talked that way. She worried that Grandma would send her away. Grandma Roberts wasn't really her grandmother; she was her foster mother. She had been taking care of Jackie and her sisters since the county took them away from their mother. It seemed to Jackie that she was always in trouble and in danger of being sent away.

Later that day after school Jackie went to play with her friend Seneca. Jackie loved it at Seneca's. Seneca had a mother, a father, and even a real grandmother. It was just the kind of family Jackie wanted.

"Seneca, is that you?" called Seneca's grandmother when Seneca opened the back door.

"Yes, Nannie, it's me. Jackie has come to play. Is that okay?" Seneca called back.

"Sure," her grandmother answered.

"Yum!" exclaimed Seneca. "Chocolate chip cookies! Have some, Jackie . . . I'll get some milk." Clutching cookies and glasses of milk in their hands, Seneca and Jackie went into the living room with Nannie.

"Hi Nannie!" said Seneca. She gave Nannie a loud "mmupf" kiss on the cheek.

"Hi, sweetie. Hello, Jackie. How are you?" Nannie said brightly.

"Hi, Mrs. Ferguson. I'm fine," Jackie answered. Jackie looked around the living room. She loved it in here. In the summertime Nannie always had roses from the garden in vases. She kept a tall glass jar filled with rose petals on one table. Whenever Jackie took the lid off the jar the sweetest, spicy smells would drift out. Jackie always thought of Nannie when she smelled roses.

In the dining room was a china cabinet filled with sparkling crystal glasses and plates with flowers painted on their edges. In one corner of the room stood a metal stand with glass shelves. On the shelves were little porcelain animals: cardinals, chickadees, deer, raccoons, chipmunks. This was Nannie's collection.

The walls were covered with family pictures. Just outside a window near Nannie's chair was a bird feeder. Nannie always had stories to tell Jackie about the birds. She talked about them as though they were people. She would lean forward in her rocker and shake a finger to make it clear that, "Some birds are good, like wrens and bluebirds, and some are bad, like those darned old blue jays who chase the little birds and scatter the seed." Nannie would say all this with great seriousness. Then she would wink at Jackie and give a little laugh.

Jackie loved being around Nannie. She was such fun. Jackie could tell that Nannie seemed to care about everything and everyone so much. She felt like she could talk to Nannie about anything.

When Seneca went upstairs to change out of her school clothes that afternoon, Jackie stayed behind to talk to Nannie. She was feeling very worried. What her foster mother had said had been in her mind all that day. "Cain't nobody help this child the way she is. Cain't nobody help . . . ."

"Is something the matter, Jackie?" Nannie asked.

"No . . . Yes . . . ," Jackie stammered. She had to tell Nannie how she felt. "I wish you were my grandma," she said sadly.

Nannie held out a hand for Jackie and gently pulled her close. Jackie sat down on the stool next to Nannie's rocker and began to talk to her. Tears trickled down her cheeks, but she didn't mind. This was what she wanted—to tell someone how bad she felt.

Jackie told Nannie how much she wanted a real mother. One who would sit and talk with her, brush the tangles from her hair, make good dinners and cookies, laugh and play with her, make pretty curtains for her bedroom window, and hug her everyday—like Nannie did with Seneca. "Even though you aren't Seneca's mother, you're like one," Jackie said.

Nannie sat forward in her rocker and said quietly, "You know, when I was a girl I lived on a farm. We had lots of cats living in our barn. Sometimes a mother cat would get sick and die or run off leaving her kittens without a mother. There always seemed to be at least one or two mother cats who would take the baby kittens in as if they were their own. Sometimes several of the mother cats would help the kittens at one time. They were like foster mothers. I think that is the way it is for you. There's your foster grandma, me, and others who can be mothers for you. Maybe you could think of us as being like the mother cats in the barn. You have a whole group of mothers." Nannie sat back in the rocker. "What do you think?" she said to Jackie.

"A group of mothers. Like mother cats and I'm their special kitten. Hm-m-m." Jackie was smiling now.

"And can you be one of the mother cats?!" Jackie asked.

Nannie laughed and said, "I think I already am."

AUSTIN LEARNS ABOUT SEIZURES

Austin Draper was 4 years old. It was his bedtime and he was taking Raggedy Andy to bed with him.

"Andy, why aren't you talking? . . . Mommie, Andy's okay; he's just tired," said Austin.

"I know he is and so are you. That is why you're getting tucked into bed," answered his mom.

"Goodnight, Mommie. Don't let the bed bugs bite."

"Goodnight, Austin. Sleep tight. Don't let the bed bugs bite."

Mrs. Draper clicked off the lamp by Austin's bed.

"Mommie?" Austin called to his mother.

"Hmmm?" she answered.

"Do firemen have seizures?" he asked.

"No," she answered.

"Does the ambulance man have seizures?"

"No, because he couldn't safely drive his ambulance if he did. That's why Mommie never drives a car. Most people don't have seizures." Then his mother added, "You don't have seizures either."

"Good," Austin said. Yawning he rolled over, placing his arm over Andy and went to sleep.

"Sweet dreams, honey," his mother said as she pulled his bedroom door closed.

Things were starting to make sense for Austin now that his mom was telling him about the seizures she and his dad sometimes had. Yesterday she had told him that the seizures were part of an illness. The seizures made it difficult for her and for his father to see, hear, talk, or do things when they were having them. Though she told Austin the name of the illness was epilepsy, Austin was more interested in how he could know his mom was having a seizure.

"I'm having a seizure when I look down at the floor and close my eyes for a long time. I'm having a seizure when I get very quiet and don't talk to you when we are building stations for your train. I was having a seizure the other morning when you brought Percy, Anna, and Tommy Train to me. That's why I didn't play with you or talk to you."

When Austin asked, "But why do you have seizures?" his mother answered, "Because I have a scratch on my brain inside my head. It's like the one on your knee except you can't see it." She let Austin examine the top of her head and assured him the scratch inside didn't hurt. She told him that she did not need a Band-Aid for the scratch, but took medicine instead.

That evening during dinner Mr. Draper had a seizure. It began with Mr. Draper saying, "I sei- - -zure." Then he didn't say anything for a long time.

"Bob, can you talk?" Mrs. Draper asked him. He said no by shaking his head.

Mrs. Draper told Austin that his father was having a seizure and would be able to talk in a little while.

Austin was worried. He wanted to know if his father could talk to him. "Daddy? Are you okay?" There was no answer so he tried again. "Daddy?"

After a while Mr. Draper said slowly, "My head hurts." He left the table to lie down on the sofa. When he got up about 15 minutes later, he was fine.

Austin's parents were telling him about seizures so he would understand why his mom and dad sometimes suddenly stopped talking to him or playing with him.

Most of all they wanted to be certain that Austin was safe when they were having seizures and couldn't look after him.

Two days later on a Saturday morning, Mrs. Draper and Austin were riding home on a bus after having gone shopping. The big orange and white bus pulled up to the bus stop near their house. Its doors opened with a "whoosh." As they were about to get off, Mrs. Draper stopped next to the driver. She stood there in the aisle of the bus, not moving or saying a word. Austin did not know it, but his mother was having a seizure. He began to worry that if they did not get off right then, the bus driver would close the bus doors and drive on.

Austin tugged on his mother's coat sleeve and said, "Come on, Mom. This is where we get off!" As he started down the steps of the bus, he suddenly felt someone pushing him out the bus door and onto the sidewalk, where he fell down. That someone pushing him was his mother. She had lost her balance from the seizure and was stumbling down the bus steps behind him. Mrs. Draper fell onto Austin. She wasn't able to talk to him.

It was a blur of motion after that for Austin. People from inside the bus, the driver, police, and paramedics were suddenly around Austin and his mother. Austin remembers that he was crying.

The paramedics laid his mother on a stretcher, strapped her on securely, and gently lifted her into the emergency van. Someone, a policewoman he thought, took hold of the arm on which he wore his Medic Alert bracelet and read the message on the bracelet. "He's her son," she said. "His mother has epilepsy, but he doesn't."
Then one of the paramedics helped Austin into the van with his mother. Mrs. Draper did not need to go to a hospital that day. Instead the paramedics drove them back to their home.

Austin is 6 years old now. Sometimes he and his mom talk about that day she had the seizure while getting off the bus. Austin likes to remember the equipment they saw in the emergency van, especially the telephone that could be used for calling ahead to the hospital.

He has a whole set of toy emergency vans, ambulances, fire engines, police cars and rescue helicopters. He uses them to play emergency and rescue games in his bedroom.

Most of the time Austin doesn't think about seizures. His mom says her new medicine helps her have fewer seizures. His dad doesn't have many seizures either anymore.

Austin is glad he knows what is happening when his mom or his dad stops talking to him or stops playing right in the middle of some exciting game. He likes it that his mom changes his baby sister on the floor and carries her in a cloth pouch so that she won't be dropped if his mom does have a seizure. He feels safe.

Austin and his mom still say good night in the very same way:

"Good night, Mom. Don't let the bed bugs bite you."

"Good night, Austin. Sleep tight. Don't let the bed bugs bite you."

THE DOLPHIN'S DREAM

Once upon a time in the sea a mother dolphin left her baby with the other mother dolphins to swim out in search of food. On this day this mother dolphin was eaten by a shark who was itself looking for food.

The baby dolphin was sad and frightened for a long time after the death of his mother. As the baby grew older he was told about his mother's death and about the dangers of sharks, but nothing the dolphin learned about the ways of the sea helped him to feel happier. Often the young dolphin would not eat his dinner when the pod (the group of dolphins to which the young dolphin belonged) was eating. He rarely rested quietly with the others. Instead, he swam restlessly back and forth.

This young dolphin did not learn his lessons quickly like the other dolphins his age. He spent most of his time feeling sad and dreaming about his mother. When other dolphin children were leaping high above the waves, somersaulting and playing tag, this unhappy dolphin circled round and round the others by himself. He was almost never playful. It wasn't long before the other dolphins did not try to play with this one.

The pod tried to help the young dolphin by choosing one of the dolphin families to take care of him. But the dolphin continued to miss his mother and became even more unhappy. What he found most difficult was living in a family where he was the only child who had not been born there. The dolphin resented that the other young dolphins in the family should have been so lucky as to be with their real parents. He felt angry and hurt, as if there was something <u>wrong</u> with him.

He took to nipping and butting the other dolphin children in the family, especially the younger ones. He would frighten them by pretending he was a shark searching for dolphins to eat.

The Dolphin's Dream

Sometimes when young sharks would swim near the pod, the dolphin would play tag with them. The dolphin did not fear the young sharks because he knew they did not swim as fast as dolphins. The dolphin would imagine he was one of the sharks—powerful and dangerous.

The more he swam with the sharks, the more he believed he was a shark and not really like the other dolphins. He thought of himself as frightening and <u>bad</u>.

Dolphins don't sleep; instead they have rest times where they float just beneath the surface of the sea, allowing themselves to rise to the surface every few minutes to breathe in and out through their blowhole before slowly sinking down below the surface of the sea to continue their rest.

It was during one such rest that this motherless dolphin had a dream. He dreamt that the sea all around the resting pod glowed green from the moon's light. Suddenly, in the dream, the young dolphin was stirred alert by the awareness that something was watching him. Out of the shadowy water beyond the moon's glow, swam one of the older dolphins of the pod. The young dolphin recognized the older dolphin as being one of the Wise Ones the pod followed in times of danger and when decisions were being made for the good of the pod. It was the Wise Ones who had decided he should have a foster family.

In the dream the older dolphin swam close to the young one and said, *"We know you miss your mother, little one. That is as it should be. But you should know that the pod is part of your family; the pod is family for all of us. There is nothing you need do to be one of us. You are not a shark. You are your mother's child and our child. We love you."*

The young dolphin remembered the dream when he was roused from his rest. He knew that he wanted to be in a family, just as the Wise One had said. He also knew he couldn't become a shark, even if he wanted to—and he didn't.

As the days and weeks passed, the young dolphin remembered the dream and the old dolphin's words: *"We love you. You are one of us. There is nothing you need do.We love you."*

During rest times he liked to let those words float through his mind over and over, like one of the lullabies his mother used to sing to him in the night. *"We love you. You are one of us. There is nothing you need do. We love you."*

In time, the dolphin decided to let himself join the pod and his family. It wasn't easy at first for the dolphin to know how to be a part of family, since he had had so much practice acting like a shark, but he just kept remembering what the Wise One had told him in the dream that moonlit night: *"There is nothing you need do. You are one of us. We love you."*

TWO BROTHER LIONS

Once upon a time a most peculiar happening took place in the forest. Two brother lions came walking along a road arguing loudly. The two lions were tied together by a long rope.

"Why do you follow me everywhere I go?" the younger lion roared at the other. "I am old enough to take care of myself."

"Oh little brother," said the older lion in reply. "It is my responsibility to help you in every way I can until you are old enough and wise enough to take care of yourself, for you know there are many dangers for those who do not know the ways of the world as I do. And . . . ."

"Shut up!" screamed the younger brother. "I don't want you as my brother! Untie that rope and let me go!"

"Don't talk to me that way, little brother," replied the older brother lion. "You are insulting and rude. I will not untie the rope that holds us together. It was our parents who told me I should take care of you and I'm going to do just that." He was feeling <u>very</u> unappreciated.

The younger brother lion was trembling with rage. "I won't listen to you! And I won't let you be my brother! You are ruining my life! Untie that rope—I can take care of myself!"

Just at that moment he saw an old sycamore tree by the side of the road. In its trunk was a large hole. Not wanting to listen to his brother a moment longer, the young lion sprang from the road and thrust his head in the hole.

What a peculiar sight it was indeed. Two brother lions—one standing in the middle of the road and the other with his head stuck inside a tree trunk— a rope tying them together by their hind legs.

"Little brother, don't do that," said the older brother lion.

"Go away! I will lead my life perfectly fine without you!" came the muffled reply from the tree trunk.

So there the brothers stayed for three days and nights. They became quite tired and hungry. No animals would come near the lion standing in the middle of the road. There was nothing at all to eat inside the sycamore tree, except an occasional ant which the younger lion would not eat.

A monkey sat high up in the sycamore tree watching in puzzlement the two lions on the road below. Finally the monkey climbed down and tapped on the tree trunk with a stone.

The younger lion, thinking it was his brother tapping, called out, "Go away. I can get along very well without you."

The monkey answered back, "Excuse me, Mr. Lion; I am not your brother. I am the monkey from up in the tree. I am wondering why you are so unhappy."

"Why am I unhappy?! Can't you see how my brother is ruining my life! He refuses to untie that rope he has put round my leg." The lion said this all the while keeping his head firmly planted inside the tree trunk.

"I have one more question then," said the monkey.

"What is it?" answered the lion, sounding very annoyed.

"Why is it that you do not untie your end of the rope yourself?" the monkey asked.

The lion did not answer.

But after a while the lion pulled his head out of the tree trunk, untied the rope from around his leg, and walked away down the side of the road. And then the older brother lion untied his end of the rope and walked along beside him, but on the other side of the road.

In time, the two brother lions became friends and helped each other.

HILTON'S KNOCKING KNEES

It was Promotion Day for pelicans in the Glider Class. Hilton knew he would not be promoted unless he could dive into the sea—and he was afraid to dive. If he dove into the water he would be promoted to Sea Bass. If he didn't, he would have to stay with the Gliders and then the bigger pelicans would tease him and call him names. They would tell him to go sit on the beach with the sea gulls.

Hilton had never admitted he was afraid to dive; instead he tried to act like he couldn't wait to make his dive. He acted like he already was a Sea Bass. He bragged about how great he was going to be at catching fish.

He made fun of others in his class. "You couldn't make a dive if they gave you a slide to slide down on!" he shouted at one of the Glider Class pelicans preparing to take off.

"Pauly is so scared to fly he poops on the dock when he even thinks about it," he snorted at another of his classmates. Some of the pelicans laughed at the things Hilton said. A few of the pelicans made jokes just as Hilton was doing, but most of the Gliders were busy adjusting their diving caps and goggles, getting ready for their dives. Some pelicans didn't say anything, but shook like they were cold.

When Hilton heard anyone say they were "scared" or "afraid," he immediately said something to them like, "Go to the end of the line, scaredy-cat."

Suddenly over the loudspeaker came their teacher's voice saying, "The next three up will be Beaufort, Hilton, and Royal. Five minutes to get ready." When Hilton heard the announcement he became so frightened he could barely stay on his feet. His legs shook so hard his knees knocked together. He turned around to Royal, whose name had also been announced as "next up," and said in a shaky voice, "You—you go ahead of me, Royal. I . . . I . . . I've got to adjust my goggles." What Hilton said wasn't true, but it worked. Royal agreed to dive ahead of Hilton.

Then Hilton felt a wingtip on one of his shoulders. It was his teacher. Bending down close to Hilton he said in a whisper, "My knees knocked together like yours the first time I tried to dive."

"M-m-m . . . my knees are . . . are not . . . knock . . . knock . . . knocking," Hilton stammered. This was said loud enough that the other pelicans in the Glider Class stopped what they were doing and looked over at him.

The teacher stood up tall and in a strong voice said, "May I have your attention, Gliders? Will everyone who has ever been so afraid to make a dive that their knees knocked together, please sit down on the dock." Only Hilton was left standing.

If pelicans could blush, Hilton's face would have been red with embarrassment, because the entire class could see his knocking knees.

"Oh-h-h, Hilton! We see your knees!" they glee-fully called out.

After what seemed like the longest moment of his life, Hilton let his knees bend and he sank to the floor like the other pelicans. He felt so alone and ashamed of himself.

"Why am I such a coward?" he lamented.

Then he heard the others shouting out things like: "Hooray Hilton!" "Attaboy Hilton!" "Welcome to the Pelicans-with-Knocking-Knees Club!" "Keep your eyes closed when you dive—it's not so scary that way . . . we do!"

From then on, Hilton didn't have any trouble say-ing he was afraid when he was. He discovered that he felt less afraid just by saying so.

HEN AND HER DUCK

Once upon a time Hen was shopping at the market. She strode along putting things in her basket until she came upon a cage filled with young ducklings. Hen said to herself, "A duckling is just what I want, for I am lonely and would like a companion." So Hen bought a pretty young duckling and took it home in her basket.

Hen took very good care of her duckling. In time it grew into a glossy white duck with lovely golden feet and a bright orange bill. Hen was very proud of her beautiful Duck.

Hen loved Duck very much. She wanted Duck to be just like her, and she tried to be just like Duck. Hen gave Duck a shopping basket just like her basket. She even tied a ribbon and flower around Duck's neck to match her own.

Hen wanted so much to be like Duck that she practiced waddling when they walked on the road to market. Hen imagined that she and Duck looked so fine. The other animals in the village leaned over the fences along the road and chuckled and guffawed at how silly Hen looked waddling like a duck, but Hen never noticed.

Hen tried to convince Duck to walk like her—like a hen, but Duck only wanted to waddle—like a duck. Duck appreciated the good care Hen took of her, but she preferred just to be herself.

Each time Hen and Duck went to market, they had to cross a small stream. They did this by stepping on stones which had been placed in the stream to help travelers go from one side to the other.

One spring day the stream was flowing over the stones because it had rained the night before. When Hen and Duck came upon the stream on their way to market, the stones were far underwater and could not be stepped on to cross the stream.

Hen said, "Never mind, my dear. We will just paddle across."

Duck did not think "paddling across" was a good idea for Hen. After all, Hen was not really a duck.

Hen would not listen to Duck. "Oh poppycock, Duck! I have webbed shoes which make my feet just like yours," said Hen. Indeed, Hen did have webbed shoes on her feet. She had made them just that day from the straw in the hay fields.

So Duck stepped into the stream and paddled across.

Hen stepped into the stream and was never seen again.

Moral of the story: The journey of life is most successfully made in one's own shoes.

HELP FOR CALIPH

The older wolf pups were gone into the high grass country to practice hunting. It was summer and the mice would be abundant.

Caliph and the other wolf pups born that spring had watched the older ones go single file up the trail and over the top of the hill. They were alone.

The pups yawned and stretched out in the morning sun at the entrance to the den. There was nothing to do because their mother had told them clearly, as she always did, to stay in the den when she was away teaching the older children. With nothing to do, the pups went to sleep.

Then, before the first hawk was circling in the new day's sky, a single brown wolf came out of the woods toward the den. This wolf had been coming to the den each morning after Caliph's mother and the older wolves had gone. Caliph looked forward to the brown wolf's appearance, because they would play together.

However, all was not as it should be. Each morning the lone wolf led Caliph and his brothers and sisters farther and farther from the den. Caliph remembered that his mother had told him to stay at home, but he liked to play.

Each time the wolf came he poked and pushed the pups in ways that didn't feel right to them. When Caliph finally said, "Stop, don't play that way! I want to go home," the older wolf laughed and called him a sissy. Then he lowered his head and said in a low growling voice, "You can't go back now because I'll tell on you. Your mother will be angry and she will punish you." What's more, the older wolf threatened to hurt all the pups if they told. Caliph was afraid, so he didn't say any more.

From then on, the pups did as the older wolf said. They felt guilty because they knew they were disobeying their mother. What were they to do?

Caliph was frantic. He knew he had to do something, but he didn't know what he could do. He did not want to play with the older wolf anymore. What was he to do?

One night the help Caliph needed came in a most surprising way. He was sitting alone on a rock near the den, looking up at the moon. He was so worried. Finally, almost in a whisper he said, "Please help me. I don't know what to do." Something moved on a tree branch not far from him. "Who-o loves you?" asked a voice in the darkness.

Caliph jumped to his feet trembling! The fur along his back bristled up. He was frightened. Caliph stared straight ahead until he saw the big yellow eyes of the Great Horned Owl who lived in the woods. The owl was sitting on a tree branch.

"Who loves you?" said the owl again.

"Why . . . why my mother loves me. But . . . ."

"And does she love you even when you disobey her?" the owl asked. His big yellow eyes glowed even brighter as he spoke.

"Yes, I think she does," Caliph answered again.

The Great Horned Owl spoke once more. "Tell her what has been happening. Everything will be

all right. She loves you." The owl winked one of
his great eyes closed and open. Then he was
gone.

Caliph gave out a lusty howl, and turned and
scampered back into the den!

He did tell his mother. And everything did turn
out all right.

BEN'S STORY

Ben stood on the back porch with his fish bowl nestled in his arms. The water in the bowl sloshed gently back and forth, causing the two goldfish floating on top to glisten in the morning sun like two maple leaves fallen from a branch in the fall. Ben had to decide how to say good-bye to his fish.

Spinner and Bottom were alive last night. Now they were dead. Ben didn't know why they died. When he picked up the fish food this morning to feed them, they were floating on their sides. Gone.

A friend's mom had flushed his guppies down the toilet when they died. But Ben didn't want Spinner and Bottom to be just flushed away. That wouldn't be right. Spinner and Bottom had been his pets—he had had them since they were baby fish in the tank at the pet store. "Besides," he thought, "you just don't stop caring about someone, even a goldfish, because it dies."

Ben set the bowl down on the porch step and went back in the house. He went to his bedroom and from his dresser drawer, took the empty plastic toothbrush box he had been saving.

Then he opened the Tinkertoy can in the box where he kept his blocks and pulled out two of the sticks. He slid them in the back pocket of his jeans.

Next he picked up his pocketknife and went to the kitchen. He found his mother's string ball in a drawer and cut off a piece.

Finally, Ben picked up a paper napkin and together with the other things he had collected, went out the back door to the step where he had left the fish bowl.

Ben carried the bowl to the flower garden which ran along the driveway. He chose a spot under the shade of the elm tree that grew close by and sat down on the edge of the driveway.

Ben had never been to a funeral or buried a pet before, but he had an idea for how to say good-bye to Spinner and Bottom.

First, he tied the two Tinkertoy sticks together to form a cross like in church. Then he opened the toothbrush box, folded the paper napkin like a blanket, and placed it in the box.

He hesitated a moment before dipping his hands in the water to take the fish out. Ben told himself that it wasn't really scary to pick up something that was dead. "And besides," he thought, "I was their friend. I took care of them."

He laid the two fish in the box, folded the rest of the napkin over them and pressed the plastic lid back onto the box until it clicked shut. Tears trickled down his cheeks. He wiped a sleeve across his eyes, swallowed, and went ahead with his work.

With the teaspoon he carefully scooped out enough dirt to form a hole large enough for the plastic toothbrush box and set it down in the hole he had dug. Then he began spooning dirt over the box. Ben didn't really like putting the dirt over the box, because he felt like he might be hurting the fish, even though they weren't alive any longer. But he went ahead until the hole was filled.

The cross stood up nicely next to where Ben's fish were buried. But he thought it needed something more to be complete. Ben brought out a small can of yellow paint from the garage and painted the cross yellow.

It was done. The fish were buried and their grave was marked so he would always know where they were.

Ben smiled. This was just the way he wanted to say good-bye.

SPECIAL KITTEN

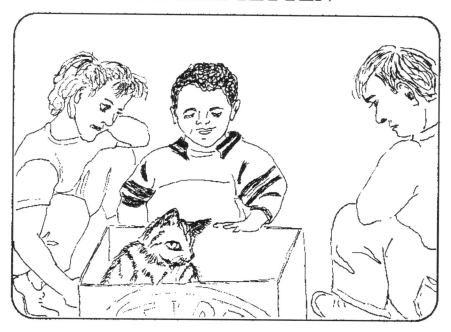

"Yes, Darnell, I think you could have a kitten."
Darnell Key could hardly believe what his mother
was telling him. A kitten!

"Oh, I hope they're not all taken," he thought.
Darnell had been watching the mother cat growing fatter with her kittens inside her each week
when he and his mother came to the grocery store
to shop. He had been wishing for a kitten the
whole time.

Just then the manager came round the corner of
the aisle and Darnell stepped in front of him to

ask about the soon-to-be-born kittens. The manager seemed to know just what Darnell was going to ask, because he reached into the back pocket of his pants and pulled out a small spiral notebook and pencil. "Let's see . . . I bet you want your name added to the list of people wanting a kitten," he said smiling broadly.

"Yes sir! Are there any kittens left?" Darnell asked breathlessly.

"One, two, three, four . . . . You're number five. A big mother cat like this ought to have at least five kittens. I'll put your name on the list."

Darnell was so excited he could hardly sleep that night. He hadn't slept well on many nights before that night because of what had happened in his family. His mother was worried about him and was hoping that a kitten would help him to feel better.

What had happened was that Darnell's aunt Ariel had been hurt in a car accident. One of her arms had something wrong with it. Because of the injury, Aunt Ariel was having to learn to write with her other hand.

Finally the kittens' birth day arrived. It was a sunny Saturday morning and Mrs. Key was doing her grocery shopping. The mother cat wasn't sunning herself in the front window as she usually did. The store manager saw Darnell and called out to him, "They're here!" He led Darnell and his mother to the stockroom at the back of the store. Just inside the swinging doors was a big cardboard box on the floor. Inside lay the yellow tiger-striped mother cat and her five kittens. "Five kittens. One, two, three . . . four, five. I am getting a kitten!" Darnell exclaimed.

He asked for one of the two white kittens, but they were already asked for. So he chose the yellow tiger-striped kitten that looked just like her mother.

Darnell came back many times to watch the kittens in the weeks that followed. He would have to wait until the kittens were old enough (about 6 to 8 weeks) to be taken from their mother before taking his kitten home.

The kittens were only a week old when Darnell noticed that one of the white kittens had a short front leg. The kitten stumbled and fell down more than the others, though they were all very small and none of them could stand very steadily. Darnell worried that the kitten might not live, or might not be able to take care of itself like the others could.

His mother and the store manager looked down at the kitten, which was then nursing from its mother. Mrs. Key said she felt sorry for the little kitten. The store manager said, "Well, those things just happen. But I bet he'll find ways to hold his own with the others." Darnell felt better when he heard the store manager's words: "He'll find ways to hold his own . . . ." Darnell remembered that his aunt Ariel was learning to write with her other hand.

"Maybe it won't be so bad for the white kitten to have a short leg after all," Darnell thought.

Soon all of the kittens had their eyes open and were charging around and over their mother and each other. They sneaked up from behind and pounced on one another, rolling over and over, biting and clawing in playful wars. Darnell's yellow kitten seemed to recognize the smell of his hand quickly and tried to climb out of the box to see him when he squatted down next it. But it was the kitten with the short leg Darnell watched the most.

The kitten with the short leg did have ways to hold his own with the other kittens. He delighted in climbing on top of his mother and flinging his body onto the back of some unsuspecting kitten he was stalking. Other times he would roll on his back and let one of his brothers or sisters hold him down as if he were defeated in their battle. Then he would kick hard and fast with his strong back legs and send them cartwheeling across the box. Darnell thought that the three-legged kitten got along fine—he just did things differently, that was all.

Darnell had begun to think of each kitten as being special. *Special* was the word the store manager used when he talked about the kittens. Some were short. Others had long tails. One had an extra claw on each foot. And one had a short leg. *Special*. Darnell supposed you could think of people that way too, even Aunt Ariel. Aunt Ariel had to write with her other hand. Maybe she was *special* too.

When Darnell and his mother arrived to take his kitten home, the store manager was there and smiling. "So this is the day! Great!" he said. "Oh, by the way, as you leave, pick up a box of kitten chow, compliments of the store."

Darnell ran to the storeroom and there sat his kitten in the box. All of the other kittens were gone. Darnell picked up his kitten and held him securely in his arms. His mother picked up the box of kitten chow the manager had set out for them and they walked to the front door of the store.

"Who got the white kitten with the short leg?"
asked Darnell.

"Why, the store did," smiled the manager.

He pointed toward the front window and said,
"See." Sure enough, the kitten with the short leg
was sitting next to its mother in front of a sign in
the window which read, "*SPECIAL, KITTEN
CHOW*." The kitten was sitting directly in front
of the last word of the sign—*CHOW*—so that the
sign just seemed to say, "*SPECIAL KITTEN*."

"I think that's what you ought to call him,"
Darnell said to the store manager.

"What name is that?" asked the manager.

"*SPECIAL KITTEN*," answered Darnell.

The store manager laughed. "*SPECIAL KITTEN*.
Yes indeed. Just the right name. We're all special
and so is he."

THE BOY AND THE CROW

There once lived a boy with his family in a house next to a woods. One morning when he and his friends were playing he ran into the woods and lost his way among the trees. He could no longer see or hear his friends. The boy was lost.

At first the boy walked along a path that he thought would take him back to his friends.

The path only led him deeper into the woods. The boy felt afraid. He worried that he would never find his way back and that he would never see his friends or his family again.

He ran through the bushes calling out for his friends. He heard no answers to his cries for help and instead was met with scratches from the bushes on his arms and legs.

The scratches stung. He felt very tired, and most of all very lost. The boy dropped down on the ground next to the foot of a great oak tree and commenced to cry, "I'm lost forever. I'll never see my mother, or my father, or my sister, or my brother, or my friends again. I don't know how to get home."

Overhead a crow flew to a branch in the oak tree, cocked his head to one side and looked down at the boy. The bird began to caw. He almost seemed to be talking to the boy. However, the boy was so exhausted and afraid that he could not listen to the crow and instead fell fast asleep.

The boy dreamed in his sleep that a beautiful, strong crow picked him up, placed him on its back and flew high above the woods. He dreamed the sky was sunny and clear above the woods and that he could see his house, his family,

and his friends. In his dream he asked the crow
to take him home, but the bird refused, saying,
"You already know everything you need to know
to find your own way home. You will be all
right."

When the boy awoke from the dream he remembered what the crow had said, "You already know
everything you need to know to find your way
home. You will be all right."

Up above in the oak tree the crow cawed and flew
off through the woods.

The boy jumped to his feet and exclaimed, "I
know what I'll do!" He grabbed a low growing
branch of the tree and began climbing toward the
top of the tree. From the top he looked into the
woods until he recognized the path he had taken
to get to where he was. He quickly climbed down
the tree, found the path, and started for home.

The crow appeared once more overhead and
called out, "Caw! Caw!" The boy called back, "I
understand! I can find my own way home!"

THE UNHAPPY PRINCESS

One afternoon a young princess sat looking for-
lornly out of her bedroom window. She was not
happy. Nothing was the way she wanted it to be.
Just as another tear was starting to roll down one
of her cheeks she saw something most surprising
in the afternoon sky. Something small and glittering was arching across the blue sky. It looked
like a woman . . . a mother . . . a fairy godmother!
It was the princess's fairy godmother!

"Over here, Fairy Godmother! Here I am!" she
called out. And sure enough the fairy godmother
landed next to her with an "umph!"

"Oh my, I'm not so good at landings," her fairy
godmother laughed. "I'll get better with practice," she chuckled. With that she smoothed her
curly red hair, straightened her starry veil, and
rubbed some smudges off the toes of her gold
satin slippers. Then she sat down on the edge of
the princess's bed. "I heard you crying. What is
the matter?" asked the fairy godmother.

The princess told her that she was unhappy
because nothing was like she wanted it to be.
When the fairy godmother asked what it was that
wasn't as she wanted it to be, the princess put her
head down and cried, "I can't say."

"Oh, I see," said the fairy godmother softly.
"Now here is what I want you to do," she continued. "I am going to leave this easel and these
paints and brushes here for you. By this time
tomorrow I want you to paint a picture about why
you are so unhappy. Will you do that?" The
princess nodded her head. Yes, she would paint a
picture about why she was so unhappy.

After the fairy godmother had flown away, the
princess sat down to paint. She quickly painted a
band of green grass across the bottom of the
paper and a bright yellow sun in one corner at the
top. Then she painted a large blue house in the

middle of the page. Next to the house she painted a tree with a swing hanging down. The last thing she put in the picture was a girl in a purple dress. The girl in the picture was crying big purple tears.

The next afternoon at the same hour a small glittering spot again streaked across the sky and down through the princess's open window. "Whoopsie . . . ! I'm still coming in a little fast," the fairy godmother exclaimed as she slid across the floor.

Then she and the princess looked at the picture. "Oh yes, I can see you are very unhappy. I see the purple tears. But what is it you are so unhappy about? You know we can't figure out what to do until you say what it is."

The princess stood without saying a word for a moment. Then she took a deep breath like people do when they are about to do something they think will be really hard to do, and picked up a paintbrush. She added a window to the house and painted a black scowling face in the middle of the window. Then she painted a large woman, twice as tall as herself, and painted the woman in bright red, green, yellow, and blue.

The fairy godmother looked at the painting and said, "And what is happening?"

The princess said the face in the window was her stepfather when he yells at her and the tall woman was her stepmother telling her what to do all the time. She wished she had a family with just her mother and her father . . . even if they weren't married any longer. "But that is not what I have," sighed the princess.

"What do you have?" asked the fairy godmother.

"What do I have?" she thought. The princess sat still for a moment, then placing a fresh piece of paper over her painting, she began another picture. She painted a picture with two houses, a father, a mother. She stopped for a second, smiled broadly and said, "And also . . . ." Then she painted a baby brother, two friends, and herself laughing in a swing.

When she finished the new picture the princess said, "The first picture is still true. I don't like being yelled at. But the second picture is true too! I do have fun with my baby brother and my friends. I think I'll keep the second one on my wall. It makes me feel good!"

"Is there still anything you are unhappy about?" asked the fairy godmother.

The princess rolled her eyes upward checking to

see if she could remember anything else about which she was unhappy. "No," she said, "But aren't fairy godmothers supposed to grant their godchildren their wishes?"

Her fairy godmother smiled at her and replied, "I just did and you chose to be happy. And whenever you choose to be happy you will be. It may take some practice—like my landings—but you will get the hang of it, just like I will."

And with that the fairy godmother put one hand on her starry veil to keep it from coming off and swept away into the sky.

"Remember," she called back. "You can choose to be happy anytime you want."

WHEN THE TIGER BELIEVES

Once upon a time in a far-off place lived a young tiger. The grown-up tigers of his family fought and tore at each other all the time. When grown-ups fought, the young ones were left to take care of themselves. Often the young tiger ran into the forest to save himself.

Once when the young tiger had run deep into the forest, he was set upon by a pack of hyenas. They danced round him snarling and screaming insults at him and threatening to rip out his heart. Had he been old enough to know that the hyenas would never dare to attack a tiger as powerful as he, the young tiger might have chased the hyenas off. Instead he leaped onto a tree limb out of their reach and fell asleep, frightened and exhausted. When he awoke, the hyenas had gone.

Ever since that terrifying night, the voices of the raging hyenas have echoed in the tiger's head.

They tell him he is under a spell he can never break—that demons live inside him.

The tiger, resentful over the ways of his family and resentful that they had not protected him from the hyenas, began to fight with his family. He told them that the demons would punish them. The tiger's family was frightened by his talk and sent him away to live with other angry and hurt young tigers.

The tiger continued to threaten anyone who would bother him. The other animals around him also became afraid and pushed him away from them, just as his family had done.

After a while the tiger made friends with a lion known as Old One. Old One had come to help the young tiger. He acted differently from the others who had tried to help the tiger before. Old One listened to the tiger's stories about his life. He listened quietly as the tiger told of that night with the hyenas. He listened to the tiger tell how the demons helped him protect himself from the animals who angered him.

Old One did not try to take the tiger's demons away. Instead, he said something the tiger did not at first understand. He said, "One day you will know that you already have a spirit that helps you take care of yourself." He told the young tiger that the spirit that had made him a brave tiger, able to survive the fighting of his family and the fury of the hyenas, was still with him and would always be with him.

The young tiger began to try to believe what the Old One told him. At first, whenever he felt abandoned or attacked, he would decide that no such spirit was in him and he would listen to the voices of the hyenas calling for the demons. But as he practiced believing that he was that same brave tiger who had taken care of himself in the forest so long ago, the voices of the hyenas and their demons became softer and softer until the tiger heard them no more.

THE MOUSE WHO WAS AFRAID OF THE DARK

There once was a little mouse who slept in a baby's shoe. The shoe belonged to a girl who had long ago grown up and moved away. It was scuffed and worn, but quite comfortable for a mouse's bed. As cozy as the shoe was, it did not keep the mouse from becoming afraid of the dark.

Each night after taking her bath and brushing her teeth, the mouse sat on the sofa between her mother and father and listened to a bedtime story.

After the story she said her bedtime prayers, kissed her mother and father good night and crawled into her soft shoe.

On most nights the little mouse drifted off to sleep right away. However, one night after her father and mother had gone to sleep in their bed, the mouse climbed out of her shoe and skittered across the rug to the teddy bear leaning against the chest of drawers. She climbed up the bear and into a hole in its side to where her parents were sleeping.

The little mouse made her way through the cotton stuffing in the bear to her parents' bed. She called out, "Mom . . . mie . . . I heard something. I'm afraid."

"What did you hear, dear?" Her mother sat up and the little mouse climbed up on the bed.

In a trembling voice the little mouse said, "It sounded like someone scratching on the window . . . or something."

Her mother took her back to the shoe. She examined all the windows in the bedroom very carefully. Everything was as it should be. No cats were lurking about. Her mother couldn't find anything which would be making scratching noises.

"Everything is fine, sweetie. Go back to sleep. You'll be okay," her mother told her.

The next night the little mouse thought she saw something move in her closet. She ran to her parents' bed again. This time she cried, "Daddy! Daddy! Something moved in my closet!"

"What!? Where!?" her father said as he jumped out of bed, still half asleep.

"It's in my closet. It's moving," she told her father. The little mouse was very worried. Just as her mother had done the night before, her father took her by the hand and led her back to her shoe.

Once her father had looked all through her shoe and had made a trip all around the bedroom he said, "I think you just saw your clothes hanging from the doorknob. That is all. There is nothing to be afraid of." He then put his arms round her and gave her a hug and helped her back into her bed.

It wasn't very many nights before the little mouse asked her parents to let her sleep with them, in their bed. She was afraid to be alone in her shoe at night, but her mother and father said they would help her to feel safer in her own bed. They gave her a night-light which they plugged in next to her bed. The night-light was in the shape of a merry-go-round. Though the little mouse liked to look at the night-light and did feel safer with it turned on at night, she was still too afraid to sleep by herself in the shoe.

For a while her father told her bedtime stories after she had gotten into bed. He taught her to make shadows on the sides of the shoe, where the light from the night-light shown. He showed her how to cup her hands together to make birds, and rabbits, and angels. Sometimes he made shadows that were part of his stories. The little mouse especially liked the stories with elephants in them. She knew how to make shadows which looked just like elephants with big ears and long trunks.

The little mouse's mother helped her make places in her bed for her favorite dolls and stuffed animals to sleep. The little mouse tucked them in safe and sound every night at bedtime. Some nights she pretended the dolls and animals were afraid of the dark. She helped them to feel safe by shining a flashlight under the covers so they could see. Some nights the little mouse told stories to the dolls and animals, just the way her father told her stories.

It wasn't very many nights before the little mouse was no longer afraid of the dark.

BROTHER ALLIGATOR
LEARNS A LESSON

Late one summer afternoon when the sun was hanging low over the willow trees, Brother Rabbit was hurrying home for supper. As he passed behind the high grass along the creek near Brother Alligator's house, he heard Brother Alligator talking. Brother Alligator was talking about catching him, that very night.

"Well I'll be swannie," chuckled Brother Rabbit. "That ole gator must be crazy. Ain't no ten alligators smart 'enuf to catch me, let alone this ugly ole gator." With that, Brother Rabbit skipped along toward his house, scheming all the way on how he would teach Brother Alligator a lesson he would not soon forget.

Now, it was Brother Rabbit's habit to take his family out for a walk on summer evenings. They almost always passed by Brother Alligator's house in the creek. Sure enough, that very evening, there were Brother Rabbit, Missus Rabbit, and their twelve children hopping about in the field next to their house, catching fireflies. Brother Rabbit was acting like he had never heard Brother Alligator saying he was going to eat him that very night.

When Brother Rabbit decided they had caught enough fireflies, he put them in a pot and pressed its top on securely so no fireflies would escape. Then he picked up the pot and a pile of burlap potato sacks and hurried off toward Brother Alligator's house.

When Brother Rabbit reached the high grasses along the creek, he quickly and ever so quietly put stones in each of the sacks. The small sacks got one stone. The two larger sacks got three stones each.

He finished putting stones in the bags and pried off the lid of the pot. There were so many fireflies in the pot it looked as though it was filled with glowing gold. Brother Rabbit tipped the pot on its side and sprinkled fireflies in each sack. Then he tied the sacks shut.

Tiptoeing, so as not to be heard by Brother Alligator, Brother Rabbit set the sacks in a row along the path next to the creek. First he set out the small sacks. Behind them he set the two bigger sacks.

"Hot diggity!" he whispered to himself. "Ole gator gonna have him a supper like he's never had before." Then Brother Rabbit danced and hopped his way back to his house and his waiting family. It was time for their evening walk past Brother Alligator's house.

"Oh—Brother Alligator! Is you home?" Brother Rabbit called out in his friendliest tone of voice. "We are goin' for our evenin' walk."

Brother Alligator, hearing the rabbit, smacked his lips in anticipation of the delicious meal he thought he was about to have. "Why yes, dear friend, I am home. I do hope you brought your lovely family along with you—I do so enjoy little rabbits."

Brother Rabbit replied, "Well, thank you, dear friend. You know my children are afraid of the dark just now, so I have given each of them some fireflies to light their way through the tall grass next to your house."

"Why how smart you are, Brother Rabbit," said Brother Alligator. "I must see this lovely sight of

73

you all carrying fireflies on your walk. Wait right there, if you please."

"Why certainly. We will wait right here on the path. You'll find us easily," Brother Rabbit called back.

"Oh yes, dear friend, I expect I <u>will</u> find you easily," answered the hungry alligator. "He is one dumb bunny, is what he is," chuckled Brother Alligator as he climbed up the creek bank and through the tall grasses.

Sure enough, when Brother Alligator parted the grasses with his nose and looked up the path, he saw what he thought was the rabbit family all lighted up by the fireflies Brother Rabbit had said they were carrying.

The hungry gator opened his mouth wide and ran up the path, swallowing every last one of the sacks Brother Rabbit had set out—fireflies, stones, and all.

"Delicious!" sighed the gator contentedly. "And those rabbits don't have to be afraid of the dark anymore."

No sooner had Brother Alligator said this, than he saw Brother Rabbit and his family sitting on the path looking back at him.

"Now children," said Brother Rabbit, "you don't have to be afraid of the dark next to Brother Alligator's house anymore, because he has decided to light up the path himself." Brother Alligator was glowing brightly from all the fireflies he had just eaten. Indeed, he was lighting up the path.

"Thanks to our good neighbor, it isn't so dark around here anymore," Brother Rabbit laughed. He laughed and laughed until everyone was laughing with him—except, of course, Brother Alligator.

All the rest of that summer Brother Alligator glowed like the fireflies that filled his stomach. And there wasn't a rabbit anywhere who was afraid of the dark.

"Brother Alligator Learns a Lesson" is written in the style of the animal tales told by the Gullah people of Daufuskie Island, South Carolina.

A TALE OF TWO PARTRIDGES

THE PARTRIDGES ARE BORN

One day in the early spring, when the purple phlox were blooming along the edge of the woods, a hunter and his two dogs flushed a mother partridge from her nest. She flew far from her nest leaving two tiny eggs; she did not return. Toward evening an old barnyard hen happened along. Seeing the two eggs in the bottom of the nest, the hen eased her body over the eggs, fluffed her feathers just so, and sat down.

The next morning when the air was warm from the sun, the hen left the nest to look for something to eat. While she was off in the fields a turkey came past the nest. Feeling a little tired he sat down on the nest to rest.

The turkey and the hen were soon joined by a barnyard cat returning home from hunting in the fields. When they saw the cat they flew up into a tree for safety. But the cat was not at all interested in eating them, or the two eggs for that matter. The cat had found the nest to be very comfortable and decided to join the turkey and the hen in keeping the eggs warm.

By the time the eggs hatched, the hen, the turkey, and the cat felt as though they were the proud parents of the two baby partridges.

They named the girl partridge Quilla, because she was the first to get her feathers. The boy they named Popper, because of the popping sounds he made when he was excited.

Before the summer was over, Quilla and Popper were ready to go into the fields to learn the things partridges must know. The turkey, the barnyard cat, and the old hen decided that their two young-sters would have to leave them to learn those things and thus must go off to join a real partridge family.

QUILLA

Quilla did not want to live with another family. She had already lived with a turkey, a cat, and a hen. "I was supposed to have a partridge for a mother. It's just not fair," she said. Quilla decided then and there that she was not going to let anyone else take care of her. She was angry and she didn't care who knew it.

The first morning in her new home, Quilla dropped a bar of soap into the toilet and tried to flush it away. The bar of soap stuck in the toilet, causing the water to overflow onto the bathroom floor. When her new mother came to see what was hap-pening, Quilla said, "The soap slipped out of my hands. It was an accident. Honest."

Later, at school, Quilla put her head down on her desk.

"Quilla. Please sit up," the teacher said.

"Leave me alone!" Quilla shouted. Quilla was looking for trouble that day and she was finding it.

At dinner when Mrs. Partridge asked her how her first day at school had gone, Quilla stormed, "It was terrible! I hate the teacher. I hate everybody!" Quilla jumped up from her chair, knocking it over on the floor. "And I don't want to live with you. You don't really care about me or my brother. You'll get tired of us and send us away— just like the others did."

Quilla ran from the room with tears streaming down her cheeks.

POPPER

Popper had heard the commotion in the bathroom that morning. He watched as water spilled over the top of the toilet onto the bathroom rug and their new partridge mother mopped it up.

On their way to school that morning Quilla told him, "I can't stay here. I'm going to run away."

"What's the matter?" Popper asked.

"What's the matter? Everything! We don't have a real family. We always have to move. No one cares about us."

Popper had heard Quilla talk this way before. He couldn't think of anything to say to her except, "Everyone has always tried to help us. I think the partridge family is nice."

Quilla frowned. Her eyes squinted and the corners of her mouth turned down. "They are <u>not</u> nice! You wait, they'll make us leave just like the others did. You'll see."

At noon recess, Quilla ran up to Popper and hit him hard in the stomach. "You're just like them!" she shouted at Popper. "You can leave me alone too!"

Popper couldn't say anything at first, because Quilla's punch had knocked the wind out of him. When he could talk again and his friends asked him what was the matter with Quilla, he could only say, "I don't know. She's always angry."

Popper, however, was happy. He had good friends that he played with everyday after school. His teachers wrote comments on his report card like, "Completes his assignments. Good class citizen. Popper is a delight to have in class!"

And Quilla stubbornly remained unhappy. She had few friends. Her teachers sent notes home which said things like, "Does not turn in assignments. Sleeps in class. Disrespectful!"

MRS. PARTRIDGE'S INVITATION

One evening after dinner Mrs. Partridge surprised Quilla and Popper. She told them she wanted them to be a part of her family for the rest of their growing up.

Popper smiled his biggest smile and immediately said, "Yes! ! !" This was just what he wanted.

Quilla shouted, "No! ! ! You can't make me! I won't!"

Mrs. Partridge was stunned into silence. When she spoke again she said, "Of course, you don't have to do this, Quilla. No one is going to make you be a part of this family."

"I don't believe you," Quilla hissed. Nothing more was said to Quilla about becoming a part of the Partridge family.

But Quilla watched what happened in the family closely. For months she suspected that she was being punished for saying no. Once when Mrs. Partridge forgot to do something for Quilla that she had promised, Quilla said, "You didn't forget. You just don't care about me."

Quilla found many reasons for getting angry and shouting and slamming things around. But no matter how awful Quilla acted—no matter what she said to insult Mrs. Partridge—Mrs. Partridge did not tell Quilla to leave.

Quilla had a home and a family, whether or not she wanted to believe it. It was up to her to learn that this was true.

QUILLA COMES HOME

Quilla felt completely alone after Popper decided to live with the Partridge family. Finally, on a dark and windy night Quilla flew to the ground from her bedroom window. She was running away. "I'll live on my own and take care of myself. I don't need anybody."

She hurried off across the fields. The moon slid from behind the clouds lighting the fields around her. Suddenly, on the path ahead of her, Quilla saw the shadow of a cat waiting in the night for some unsuspecting creature to wander near it.

She hid under a clump of grass but was not quick enough. The cat had seen her. Quilla's heart was pounding. She could hear the cat creeping toward her.

What Quilla didn't know was that the moment she had flown from her bedroom window, Mrs. Partridge had sensed something was wrong. She and Popper had followed Quilla through the fields and were close to catching up with her when the cat found her.

Then Quilla heard Popper calling for her. She ran from the clump of grass, but the cat was upon her before she had gone two steps. With one swipe of a paw he scooped her up—and held her against his chest. Then from inside his chest, a deep rumbling purr began. He was her old friend the barnyard cat.

The cat set his prey on the ground in front of him. Popper and Mrs. Partridge came running. They hugged Quilla tightly and told her how happy they were that she was safe.

Finally, Mrs. Partridge asked, "Will you come home with us?"

Quilla was shaking, and feeling cold in the night air she snuggled against the mother bird's soft feathered breast. "I would like to come home," she said softly. "Very much."

BURLEY'S FATHER

The great bear's claws ripped and slashed across
the smaller bear's body. She had no chance to
protect herself from his fury. In a moment she
was down. The bigger bear glared angrily at her
as she lay motionless on the ground. Then he
turned and shuffled down the mountainside, paus-
ing several times to look back at the fallen bear.
When he reached the bushes below her den, he
pushed through them and out of sight. He did not
return. A turtle dove called mournfully to its mate
from a nearby tree. There was no other sound to
be heard.

Burley remembered that awful fight and how his
father had looked back at Burley's mother lying

there on the ground. He had been very young at
the time. His father had come home angry and
had started threatening his mother. Burley had
hidden in a dark corner of the den. Now
Grandma Neerja, Burley's grandmother, was
telling him about his father.

"When you were born, your father was so proud.
As soon as you were able to leave your mother's
side he took you to the river to teach you to catch
the salmon. He made sure you were never in
water that was too swift or too deep. At that time,
nothing was more important to your father than
you and your mother. He saw to it that you both
were always safe and that you had enough berries
and fish to eat.

Grandma Neerja looked fondly at Burley. "You
are your father's image. You have a silky thick
coat, just the color of his. You even have his
broad shoulders." She paused, then said, "The
way you are now, kind and brave, is the way he
was in the beginning."

"What happened to him?" Burley asked.

Grandma Neerja continued. "He changed after he
found the trash dump outside the village. He was
different after he started going to the dump and
eating the food that was thrown there by the

humans. None of the rest of us, except for Lone Eye, your uncle, would go there. We had seen what could happen to bears that ate from the trash dump. But your father and Lone Eye wouldn't listen to us. They didn't believe anything could happen to them."

"What did happen?" Burley asked again.

"Your father and Lone Eye started going to the dump every night. At first your father brought food back for you and your mother. After a while he stopped bringing food. There were times in the dry season when there were no berries for you to eat. He even gave up fishing on the river. When your mother would tell him that you and she needed food, he would get angry and cuff and bite her."

Grandma Neerja got to her feet and paced back and forth in front of Burley. "Lone Eye lost an eye one night in a fight with other bears at the trash dump. He realized then how dangerous it was for them to be there. But your father would not listen to Lone Eye and leave the dump, even when Lone Eye pleaded for him to come home. Your father had changed."

"But you said he was kind and good," Burley said.

"The bear you saw slash your mother so cruelly was not the same bear who rolled about and

played with you in the leaves. He was no longer
the brave bear who watched over you and your
mother in storms. Eating from the dump changed
him. After that he only looked like your father,"
Grandma Neerja replied.

"Then I don't want his name! I don't want to
look like him! He was no father at all!" Burley
cried out angrily. "He didn't come back to help
my mother when he knew he had hurt her. He
hasn't ever come back. I hate him!"

Grandma Neerja moved over next to Burley and
let him lean against her side. "Burley, your father
couldn't come back after that day because the
older bears on our mountain sent him away. No
bear can be permitted to attack his own family.
He had to leave."

Grandma Neerja pulled Burley close to her with
one of her paws. When she spoke next, it was
with soft, carefully spoken words. "It is true that
your father was changed once he no longer followed the ways of the bears on our mountain and
began eating from the trash dump. He did act
mean and cruel. Eating from the dump made him
sick. Lone Eye decided to stop going to the
dump. I don't know why your father didn't make
that same choice. Maybe he had become too sick
to know that he could change."

Nothing more was said for a while. Burley just let himself feel the soft warmth of his grandmother's body. Leaves made their whispering sounds from the breezes blowing through them. From a branch lighted by the fading afternoon sun, a turtle dove called to its family.

"I wish my father hadn't gotten sick," Burley said.

"So do I," said Grandma Neerja. "But you know, Burley, we have a choice. We can remember your father as he was after he had become so sick, or we can remember him as he was when he was healthy. I choose to remember the father who took his son to the river to fish for salmon . . . the father who loved and protected his family. That's the way I like to remember him. Maybe you would like to remember him that way too."

JERRY JUMP

Jerry Jump loved to jump . . . to leap . . . to bound. He was a born jumper.

When he was just a little boy he jumped over fire hydrants, lawn sprinklers, tricycles, bicycles, wagons, lawn mowers, the family dog—and his baby sister. He jumped, bounced, ricocheted, sprang, sprung, and exploded over everything on which he took aim, which was almost everything. His family and neighbors applauded his every jump. His Uncle Sid said he must be a child prodigy.

When Jerry was five years old he was jumping fences, sports cars, and Ping-Pong tables. Everyone said his jumping was fantastic. Uncle Sid proclaimed, "No boy has ever jumped as high or as far my nephew, Jerry. The sky's the limit."

On Jerry's 8th birthday Uncle Sid boasted, "Jerry will be the best basketball player ever! Just wait until he has finished growing."

Everyone agreed. "Just wait; when Jerry is grown he will be the best basketball player ever!"

And wait they all did. Jerry had his 9th birthday, his 10th, 11th, 12th . . . 14th, 15th birthdays. He was growing up. He was jumping ever higher. But Jerry Jump was not growing tall.

Jerry Jump was still the best jumper anyone had ever seen, only now people called him "Little" Jerry Jump. Uncle Sid said, "He is the best jumper for a little guy you'll ever see." His basketball coach at school said, "Jerry could be great—if he wasn't so short."

Jerry didn't seem to notice that people were referring to him as "that little guy who jumps so good." He just kept on jumping over bushes, fences, motorcycles, and picnic tables. He could dunk basketballs whenever he wanted, which was only some of the time.

Jerry Jump

Uncle Sid asked Jerry if he was disappointed that he was not really tall.

Jerry answered, "Not really. Well sure, I have thought about it. I might be able to jump higher if I was taller—but maybe not. Anyway, it's what you do with what you've got that counts. I can jump. That is what I've got. I like to jump, so I jump. That's what I do."

GRUBB'S STORY

High in a tree in the deep of a jungle lived Grubb, a chubby green and yellow snake. Grubb knew that snakes are supposed to be long and slender like vines. She, however, was short and chunky. The older snakes said she probably would "grow out of it." The younger snakes teased her. When they saw her they would sing out,

"Fatty, Fatty, two by four—can't get through the kitchen door . . . ." Grubb did not mind being a chubby green and yellow snake nearly as much as she minded being teased about being chubby.

At first, Grubb was embarrassed by the teasing. She began to spend more time hanging alone in the trees. Parrots would mistakenly peck on her, thinking she was a bunch of bananas hanging there. Grubb felt very lonely.

Her tormenters would sing out from the jungle floor below,

"Tub-bee Grub-bee . . . Tub-bee Grub-bee . . . ."

Grubb was so heavy that sometimes tree branches would snap in half sending her crashing down to the ground with a resounding thud.

Then the young snakes would scream in delight and slither through the jungle calling out, "Help! Help! The sky is falling. Watch out for falling Grubbs."

Nothing Grubb did stopped the teasing—not getting angry and biting the other snakes' tails; not even making jokes about herself.

One day, after another limb had broken under Grubb's weight, she happened across her only real friend. Grubb was sliding her way up a tree trunk, when she thought she smelled her friend. She flicked her long tongue out to taste the air. Then she said, "Albert? Are you awake?" There was no answer. "Albert? It's me, Grubb."

A dark lump hanging underneath a leafy branch moved ever so slightly. Out of the shadows a sleepy-sounding voice answered, "I'm awake, Grubb." Then after a long pause, "What do you want?"

The dark lump was Albert, a three-toed sloth, the slowest moving creature in the entire jungle.

"Albert, I'm so unhappy," Grubb began. "Everybody laughs at me because of how I look. There isn't one other snake who is lumpy and chunky like me. I get teased all the time."

Slowly Albert turned his face toward Grubb. "I have a question," he said.

"What is it?" Grubb replied.

"What do you think would happen if you weren't unhappy about the teasing?"

"What would happen?" Grubb answered in disbelief. "If I didn't get angry, they would think I was weak or that I liked being teased. Then they would tease me more."

"Why do you believe if you weren't unhappy about the teasing you would be teased more?" Albert asked. He then proceeded to rest his head between his legs and close his eyes.

Grubb didn't know how to answer his question right then, so she asked, "Well, are you happy when animals tease you?" Albert didn't answer. He wasn't going to answer for a while. He was asleep again.

With a sigh Grubb slid out to the end of the branch, wrapped her body around it and asked herself the questions Albert had asked. "Why do I believe I would be teased more if I wasn't unhappy about the teasing?"

She thought about how Albert was often teased for being slow and sleeping so much. It puzzled her that most of the time Albert seemed happy. "I want to be happy too," Grubb thought, "but it's different for Albert. He is slow and sleepy like all sloths. I'm <u>chunky and lumpy</u> and that's not like other snakes."

Grubb felt heartbroken. Tears ran down her cheeks and fell to the ground below. A few of them landed on the back of a young snake passing by. Feeling the tears on its back, the snake looked up and saw Grubb in the tree. "Hey! Stop spitting on me, Tubby!" he shouted up at Grubb.

In an instant Grubb was slipping down the tree
trunk. "I'll teach him to call me names!"
Albert awoke to hear the angry hisses of Grubb
and her tormentor. They were nose to nose. He
started down from the tree as fast as he could
move, which of course wasn't fast at all.

A crowd of young snakes had gathered and were
taunting Grubb hoping to see a fight. "Chubby,
Tubby, Grubby couldn't get through the bathroom
door . . . !"

"Shut your mouths, you worms!" answered Grubb
hotly.

"Rub-a-dub Grubb—she's big as three men in a
tub . . . ."

Grubb was crying. When the crowd of young
snakes saw her tears they stopped their teasing.
"Hey, leave the crybaby alone," one said.

Just then Albert climbed onto the tree branch
above them. They looked up at him in surprise.
A few of the snakes laughed about his slowness
and joked that he was exceeding the jungle speed
limit. "Slow down before you hit something,
Albert," they snickered.

Grubb and the snake she had been about to fight
both began to laugh. Soon all of the snakes,

Grubb included, were rolling on the ground joking and laughing about sloths that raced about running into trees.

Finally several of the snakes announced that they had to get home because their mothers would be looking for them.

"See you. Bye, Grubb. Bye, Albert," they called out as they slid away. They sounded friendly, just as if they had never teased either Grubb or Albert.

Grubb climbed up the tree to the limb where Albert was hanging upside down. "Albert," she said, "why do the others act like they are my friends sometimes and then call me names other times?"

"Well . . . ." Albert replied. He sounded like he was getting sleepy. "I don't say it's right, but some animals seem to think there is something funny about anyone who is different from them. Teasing is what a lot of animals like to do."

Suddenly, Grubb remembered that she had laughed at Albert. "Oh, Albert, I apologize for laughing at you, but it seemed so funny to think of you <u>racing</u> about." Grubb realized that she had been laughing at Albert because he was different from her. It was just what the others had been doing to her.

Albert yawned.

"Albert, wait! Don't go to sleep yet," She poked Albert's soft body with her nose. "There is something else... I don't like being chunky."

"Well, Grubby, maybe you could decide to like yourself the way you are."

"You mean—like myself even though I'm chunky?"

"Isn't that what you want the others to do?" Albert answered.

Grubb became very quiet. Yes, that was what she wanted. And that's when she began to understand. She could like herself chunks and all! She could be happy even if she was teased!

By this time Albert had gone back to sleep. "Thank you Albert," Grubb hissed softly and climbed to a high (but sturdy) branch where bananas sometimes grow and arranged her body . . . just so. Then, tucking her head inside her green and yellow lumpy coils, she fell happily asleep.

APPENDIX :
QUESTIONS FOR ENCOURAGING
DISCUSSION OF THE STORIES

Many young persons who listen to these stories
will benefit by discussing them. However, I
always respect their desire to discuss or not discuss their reactions to a story. I believe we all do
what we believe is best for us at every moment in
time. Thus, I am delighted to listen as they
describe a memory they had while listening to a
story—and I am equally delighted to end the story
without discussion, knowing that they do not wish
to share their thoughts at that time. In this way I
hope to build a trust relationship with the listeners, knowing that some memories and associations
can be shared only when the young person trusts
me.

The following questions are offered only as exam-
ples. My guiding principle is always to follow the
interest of the young person. If I listen carefully, I
have no difficulty in knowing what questions to
ask—they flow naturally from the comments the
young person is making. Questions of this type
support the young people's thought processes and
do not divert them from the psychological work
they are doing at that moment.

Discussion in the following areas should be encouraged:

- Experiences that the listener has had which are similar to those in the story.

- Listener identification with one or more of the story characters.

- Feelings, memories, and associations the listener experienced during the story.

- Imaginings of what would take place in the story beyond its end.

Questions such as the following will help encourage discussion:

- Has something like this ever happened to you?

- How would / did you feel?

- Who in the story do you feel most like?

- If you were a character in the story who would you be?

- If you were _____ (character) what would you have done or thought or felt when? _____? Why?

- Who was your favorite (or least favorite) character? Why?

- What do you think happened after the end of the story?

- What do you think became of _____ (character)?

- Did you like the way the story ended? Why? Why not? How would you change the ending?

Statements of approval or disapproval, i.e. judgments, should not be made about what listeners share about themselves. Our beliefs about our life experiences are uniquely our own. Statements such as, "You shouldn't have felt afraid" or "Everybody would feel..." etc., teach us that we are not our own best experts about ourselves.

Empathetic responses from the storyteller (e.g., "You were really frightened when you thought you were lost") are called for, because they let the listeners know that they are being heard and understood. Use empathetic responses liberally.

AUTHOR / ILLUSTRATOR

Don Mason is a social worker in private practice specializing in child-centered play therapy and therapy for adolescents.

Living in Shaker Heights, Ohio, he is married and has three children and two grandchildren. His fascination with story telling took root while listening to his grandfather's stories about bears and boys in the woods of Alabama, grew with the stories he heard about life on the Kansas prairies, and blossomed from his imagination into bedtime stories for his children.

He holds an M.A. in social work from Indiana University.